Marine Life
of the Channel Islands

Sue Daly

© 1998 Kingdom Books, PO Box 15, Waterlooville PO7 6BQ, England.

contents

acknowledgements

I would like to thank Chris Wood for his constant encouragement and help with the 'ology bits' and without whom this book could not have been written. I am also indebted to the following people and organisations who gave invaluable help and local information: Andrew Syvret, Pete Double, Simon Bossy, Mrs B Young, Frank Gautron, Jimmy Webster, Guille-Allès Library in Guernsey, Jersey Maritime Museum and the Société Jersiaise. Graham Ackers, David George, Ray Williams and R L Manuel also assisted with species identification. Thanks also to Fay, Jez and anyone else who has had the misfortune to dive with me and my camera and to all at Jersey Underwater Centre, especially Marcus. A special thanks to Lee Durrell of the Jersey Wildlife Preservation Trust for writing the Foreword.

Finally a big thank you to my husband, Matthew, for his support and encouragement in everything I do.

All photographs and drawings by Sue Daly except Goldsinny Wrasse and *Bugula flabellata* by Chris Wood, Rock Cook by Frances Dipper and Topknot by Jo Murphy.

dedication

In memory of Jakki O'Connor who taught me how to look.

But the sea about this and the adjoining islands might be titled the kingdom of the congers, so great is the quantity taken.

Phillipe Falle 1694

foreword

As someone who has only snorkelled on coral reefs in warm tropical seas, I was amazed to learn of the beauty and richness of marine life in our own waters. I should have suspected as much, having been introduced by my husband, Gerald Durrell, to the delights of dabbling in rock pools at Corbière, but it needs an experienced diver to relate the story of the underwater world around our Islands. Sue Daly has done just that in this marvellous book.

This is much more than an identification guide, for the photographs and written descriptions make the sea come alive. Sue reveals the charms of the Candy Striped Flatworm, the Teddy Bear Crab and the Little Cuttle, who emits such perfect ink rings, and she tells of the sex lives of seahares and nudibranchs and the fatherly attitude of seahorses and pipefish. She makes note of some of the creatures only rarely found in British waters, which is a special treat for the zoologically-inclined.

This book will be an inspiration to anyone attracted to the sea – divers, snorkellers, fishermen, rock poolers and beach walkers – and to all who want to protect and nurture the natural heritage of the Channel Islands.

Lee Durrell
Jersey Wildlife Preservation Trust

Introduction

On calm summer days, the sea around the Channel Islands is blue and clear, more like the Mediterranean than the English Channel. In the winter, though, it can be wild and hostile, especially during the storms when the pounding waves break half way up the cliffs and spray is blown far inland. At times like this, it is hard to imagine how anything can live in such seas, but live it does and in an astonishing array of shapes, sizes and colours.

I have been watching these wonderful creatures for the last ten years and, even after many visits to exotic coral reefs, I remain enthralled by what I see around these islands. The aim of this book is to share my fascination for these amazing animals with fellow divers, snorkellers, rock pool explorers and anyone else with a love of the sea.

The Channel Islands

The Channel Islands lie over 160km (100 miles) off the south coast of England in the bay of St Malo and are subject to one of the largest tidal ranges in the world. During the greatest spring tides, the sea drops 12m (40ft) from high to low water, exposing many square miles of land and creating a paradise for the rock pool explorer. This huge tidal range, and the influence of the Gulf Stream, mean that the seas around the Channel Islands are rich in marine life, both in terms of diversity of species and number of individuals. Whilst none of these species is unique, a number of them are at the northernmost limit of their distribution and are rarely, if ever, found around the coast of the British mainland.

Underwater topology varies through the area. Jersey sits on a plateau which rarely reaches much more than 30m (100ft) deep until you are several miles offshore. The waters around the more northerly islands are deeper, and Sark in particular benefits from some beautiful drop-offs to more than 50m (160ft). The seabed around the islands is characterised by bedrock, boulders and smaller rocks, with areas of sand and some silt. The seabed around Sark has less silt, and this contributes to the spectacular visibility which the island's waters can offer.

The picture on the far left shows Ormers being gathered on a low spring tide on the Minquiers Reef. The main picture shows Bouley Bay on the north coast of Jersey.

The picture on page 4 shows the Point Robert Lighthouse on Sark.

Using this book

As well as being an aid to identification, I hope this book will offer the reader an insight into the remarkable lifestyles and behaviour of local marine life. Anemones that fight each other, fish that change sex, and slugs that imitate coral – all amazing stuff! Although far from comprehensive, it does cover all the major groups of marine animals to be found around the Channel Islands, including those, like hydroids and bryozoans, that are often overlooked. I have also included a brief description of each group. Latin names have only been used on their own where a common name does not exist, as is the case for many of the sponges and nudibranchs. The size given for each creature is the maximum for the species, so many of the individuals observed will be smaller. For more details of any of the animals or groups included, a list of books I have found useful is in the bibliography.

A small illustration at the top of each page will help you to identify the chapter you want to find.

Game laws and safety

The game laws for fishing and low water gathering vary from island to island. Divers are not allowed to take anything at all from the waters around Sark, nor are they permitted to take Ormers, lobsters or crawfish from any of the other islands. Scallops can only be taken under licence. There are minimum sizes for many fish and shellfish landed and strict seasons for low water Ormer gathering. For the precise regulations for each of the islands, contact the relevant department of fisheries (see Useful Addresses).

If you need to turn over rocks to look for marine life, put them back carefully to conserve the fragile environment beneath them. Keep an eye on the tide, too. During mid-tide the water will rise at nearly 3m (9ft) per hour. It is worth investing in a set of tide tables. Before diving or snorkelling from any of the islands, contact the local dive centres for advice on the best sites to visit. Even the most sheltered-looking of bays can be subject to strong tidal currents.

Conservation

All the creatures illustrated in the book need unpolluted seas to live in. The Channel Islands have an excellent record for clean water, but in many parts of the United Kingdom sewage waste, pesticides, litter and overfishing have impoverished the seas. One of the organisations that promote clean seas for all marine life is the Marine Conservation Society through its annual beach cleans and litter surveys, its lobbying and its education activities all over the United Kingdom. An active group is established in Jersey and new members are always welcome. For more information, send a stamped, addressed envelope to the address in Useful Addresses.

Do not disturb any seahorses that you encounter, and please report any sightings of these fish to Neil Garrick-Maidment at the National Marine Aquarium, The Fish Quay, Plymouth, PL4 0LH.

1 Sponges

Sponges occur in a huge variety of shapes, sizes and colours but, because they are static and often covered in silt, they are frequently overlooked. They belong to the group Porifera, which literally translates as 'pore bearer'. This refers to the network of holes through which all sponges draw water. The water is filtered for food particles and expelled through the larger pores. Sponges have no circulatory, nervous or digestive systems, making them the simplest members of the animal kingdom apart from single-celled organisms.

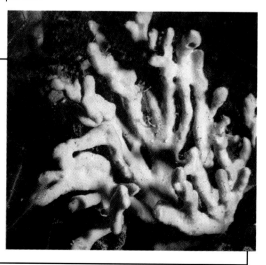

The form of a sponge can vary enormously, even within one species, according to the type of surface the sponge is attached to and the amount of water movement it encounters. This can make accurate identification difficult without carefully examining the sponge's structure under a microscope.

Sponges produce unpleasant tasting chemicals to ward off predators but are still used as a food source by various animals such as urchins, starfish and nudibranchs. Many other animals use them as a place to hide, making sponges an important part of the marine environment.

The waters around the Channel Islands contain dozens of species of sponge, some of which can easily be found in the lower rock pools. In deeper water they occur wherever there are stable, rocky surfaces for them to bore into or grow over. The sponges described here are just a few of the most common and conspicuous species.

Axinella dissimilis
Up to 15cm (6in). This common sponge forms pale orange or yellow branching fingers which are oval in section. Its surface has a velvety texture and the whole sponge has a flexible, rubbery consistency. It grows on rock faces below the kelp line and seems to prefer areas exposed to the current.

Raspailia ramosa

Up to 15cm (6in). The dark red-brown colour of this sponge is often hidden by silt. It forms branching, cylindrical fingers with small but distinct openings. This sponge is firm but flexible and grows at all depths below the low water line on rocks and boulders. It can live in fairly sheltered areas as well as those with some tidal current.

Haliclona simulans

Up to 25cm (10in). This sponge can grow as irregular encrusting sheets but is most conspicuous when it forms the round, stick-like branches shown here. It is light brown in colour with paler tips and obvious pores. It is hard and brittle and grows in the shelter of cracks and crevices in areas exposed to the current.

Haliclona viscosa

Up to 40cm (15in). This sponge grows in a series of lumpy ridges with very distinct volcano shaped holes. It is usually a distinct purple colour but can edge towards pink or brown. The surface of Haliclona viscosa is firm and smooth and it grows in rocky places below the kelp line in current-swept areas.

Elephant's Ear Sponge
Pachymastia johnstonia
Up to 1m (3.3ft) across. This is one of the largest and most conspicuous of all the sponges in the Channel Islands. It forms irregular grey lobes with obvious holes along the ridge and is firm and smooth to the touch. It is widespread on vertical rock faces from the low

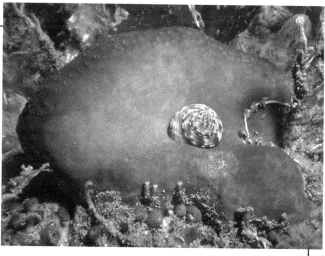

water line down. It can occasionally be found in crevices and overhangs in the lowest rock pools around the islands on very low tides. Resting on this specimen is a Painted Topshell (page 45).

Boring Sponge *Cliona celata*
Up to 1m (3.3ft) across. As its name suggests, this sponge is able to bore into the surface of soft rock and secretes an acidic chemical for this purpose. It creates a series of branching passages beneath the surface and then emerges as a bright yellow mass with very conspicuous pores and a knobbly texture. It is common in rocky areas from the low water line down. It is also known to bore into the shell of the Ormer, a process which eventually weakens the shell so much that it breaks down, leaving the Ormer vulnerable to predators.

Leucosolenia complicata

Up to 10cm (4in). This grey-white sponge takes the form of a mass of tubes projecting from a rounded cushion and is soft to the touch and very fragile. It grows in rocky areas, often under overhangs, but does not like to be exposed at low water. It can frequently be found in association with red sea weeds.

Polymastia mamillaris

Up to 12cm (5in). The body of this sponge is often covered in sediment or silt leaving only the pale yellow, almost transparent tubes visible. The body area is hard to the touch and the tubes are rigid. It often seems to be growing in areas of sand or silt but will always be attached to the rock beneath. It occurs at all depths from the low water line down.

Polymastia boletiformis

Up to 12cm (5in). This sponge forms bright yellow, roughly ball-shaped growths with tapering tube-like projections, the ends of which will close up when disturbed. It is fairly soft and flexible and lives on the top of boulders or upward-facing rocks in the edge of the kelp line and below. It can tolerate rapidly flowing currents as well as sheltered, silty areas.

Shredded-carrot Sponge
Esperiopsis fucorum

Up to 30cm (12in). This bright orange or red sponge can vary in shape from a thin encrusting sheet to a soft cushion supporting volcano-shaped pores. In very calm conditions, such as harbours and marinas, it grows long 'tassels', hence its common name. Small pieces can be found in the lower rock pools and it occurs down to the deeper edge of the kelp line.

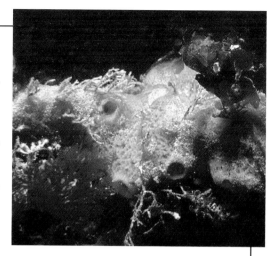

Dysidea fragilis

Up to 15cm (6in). The pale, irregular form of this sponge, together with its distinctive surface texture, makes it resemble small blobs of mashed potato. It has a soft, elastic consistency and grows in rocky areas from the low water line down. It can tolerate quite silty areas, often making it difficult to distinguish from other encrusting marine life.

Black Tar Sponge
Dercitus bucklandi

Up to 20cm (8in). The jet black colour of this sponge and its habit of bridging small cracks and crevices make it difficult to confuse with any other species. Its pores are positioned in small groups and it has an elastic, rubbery texture. The Black Tar Sponge occurs below the extreme low water line in rocky areas and caves but its colour and favoured habitat can make it difficult to spot.

Hemimycale columella

Up to 30cm (12in). This sponge grows in thin sheets and cushions on rocks and pebbles and is a delicate orange-pink colour. Its surface is very smooth and slippery with a characteristic pattern of circular holes with pale rims. It can be found in areas with some exposure to currents in the kelp line and a little deeper.

Purse Sponge
Scypha ciliata

Up to 9cm (3.5in). This small sponge forms pale yellow cylinders with a circle of longer hairs at the end. The surface of each individual is covered in fine hairs, giving it a furry appearance. It grows on rock and seaweed, often in groups, and can be found around the low water line and below.

2 Hydroids, Anemones and Corals

Hydroids, anemones and corals all belong to the group called Cnidaria. Initially they seem to have little in common with each other, but all are 'flower-like' animals that have tentacles to catch their food and stinging cells, called cnida, hence their name. Although they have no proper organs or circulatory system they do have a simple nervous system and so are considered to be higher up the evolutionary scale than sponges.

Hydroids

Due to their tiny size and lack of bright colours, hydroids are often overlooked. However, they are extremely common, particularly below the kelp line, where they often cover huge areas of the seabed. They consist of either a solitary polyp or many polyps linked together to form a colony and are an important source of food for other marine creatures, especially nudibranchs. There are many different species of hydroid in the waters around the Channel Islands with just a few of the most common varieties described here.

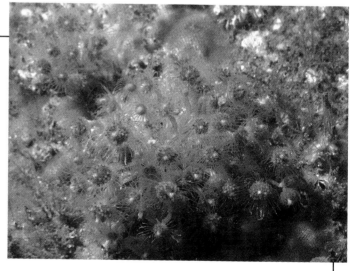

Tubularia larynx
Up to 4.5cm (1.7in) tall. This hydroid is very similar to *Tubularia indivisa* (page 17) except it does not grow as tall and the stem is branched, supporting several polyps. These polyps are pink with white tentacles and a yellow tassel in the centre. It grows on rock faces from the low water line down to at least 100m (330ft) and can also be found on the pilings in the islands' harbours and in the Gouliot caves in Sark.

Oaten Pipe Hydroid
Tubularia indivisa

Up to 15cm (6in) tall. The stiff pale yellow stem of this species supports a delicate pink, flower-like polyp. It grows in huge numbers in rocky areas and on shipwrecks in current-exposed areas. The Blanchard reef off Sark and the wreck of the Schokland off Jersey are so covered in this hydroid in spring that they appear to be fluffy. This is a favourite food source for nudibranchs, particularly *Coryphella browni* (see page 52), and by midsummer all the polyps have been eaten leaving just the stem.

On the left is a female Cuckoo Wrasse.

Sea Beard
Nemertesia antenina

Up to 25cm (10in) tall. This is a colonial hydroid with each of the pale yellow strands being made up of a chain of many tiny individual polyps, their tentacles giving it a furry appearance. It grows in clumps of strands below the low water line in rocky areas exposed to strong currents. A similar species called *Nemertesia ramosa* also lives in the same type of habitat but can be distinguished by its branching stems.

Gymnangium montagui

Up to 15cm (6in) tall. The pale chestnut branching shape of this species looks like a tiny feather. This is another colonial hydroid made up of chains of individual polyps attached to a central stem. Each one catches particles of food that are borne on the passing water currents. It lives in clumps of 'feathers' below the low water line in rocky areas.

Obelia geniculata

Up to 4cm (1.5in). This very common hydroid forms chains of polyps arranged in a zig zag pattern to produce pale coloured strands. It grows on the blades of kelp and close observation will reveal the presence of fine hair-like strands which link each of the colonies. It can be seen still attached to the kelp when it is washed up on the beach in the winter, together with the Sea Mat *Membranipora membranacea*.
(See page 57.)

Anemones

Anemones are some of the most highly-coloured animals in the sea and, as a group, are incredibly successful. They can live on rock or wood, buried in the sand and even on the shells of hermit crabs. Each one consists of a column containing the digestive cavity with an opening at one end surrounded by a ring of hollow tentacles. The tentacles contain coiled stinging cells often armed with tiny blades and barbs.

Anemones can reproduce either sexually, by releasing eggs and sperm, or asexually by splitting or growing a tiny, fully formed individual. This means that when they find themselves in a particularly favourable position they can reproduce rapidly to cover huge areas.

Around the Channel Islands anemones can be found at all depths from shallow rock pools and sandy bays to the reefs and plunging rock faces further offshore. The most stunning display of species and colours is to be found in the aptly-named Jewel Caves near the Gouliot passage in Sark.

Tube Anemone

Pachycerianthus 'Dorothy'

Tentacles up to 30cm (12in) across. Unlike most other anemones, this species lives inside a thick, mucus tube buried in the seabed. It has two distinct rows of tentacles, both of which withdraw rapidly inside the tube if disturbed. Its colour is variable, with the outer ring of tentacles often patterned with pale bands. It lives in areas of sand and shingle below the low water mark. Little is known about this hitherto undescribed species which is found in the Channel Islands and Northern France but is not thought to occur elsewhere in the British Isles.

Colonial Anemone
Parazoanthus axinellae

Up to 1.5cm (0.5in) tall. This bright yellow anemone grows in colonies with each individual joined to the group at its base. It lives below the low water line and grows on rock faces, overhangs and in caves. It is also known to grow on other static marine life such as sponges and sea squirts. This anemone is a southern species and is only found on the south-west coasts of the British Isles.

Jewel Anemone
Corynactis viridis

Up to 1.5cm (0.5in) across. The vivid, almost luminescent, colours of this anemone easily justify its name. It appears in a brilliant combination of green, pink, yellow, orange, white or brown with contrasting coloured knobs on the end of each tentacle. Even in the gloom of deep water this anemone seems to glow with inner colour and light. When it finds itself in a favourable position it reproduces rapidly by budding new individuals, producing patches of the same coloured anemone. It commonly covers large areas of rock face in exposed areas from the low water line down to about 50m (164ft).

Beadlet Anemone
Actinia equina

Up to 5cm (2in) across. This anemone is most often seen as a dark red, jelly-like blob left on the rocks when the tide goes out, but can also be found in orange. Each individual has a row of bright blue 'beads' just below the tentacles, hence the common name. Although it seems totally static, it can move around the rocks in search of food and will even fight another anemone that comes into its territory using its battery of stinging cells. The green form of this anemone has recently been found to be a separate species, *Actinia prasina*. It is found in rocky areas down to about 10m (33ft).

Strawberry Anemone
Actinia fragacea

Up to 10cm (4in). This deep red anemone is very similar to the Beadlet Anemone but grows to almost twice its size. It has crimson or purple tentacles and beautiful yellow or pale green markings on its columns that look rather like the pips on strawberries. It is found in rock pools and down to about 10m (33ft) and is a southern species confined to the Channel and south-west England.

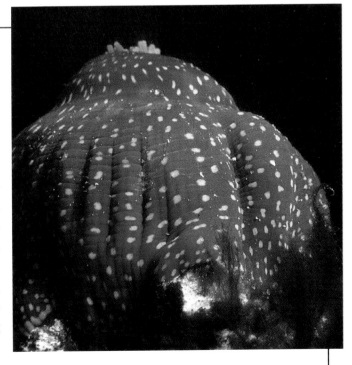

Snakelocks Anemone
Anemonia viridis

Up to 20cm (8in) across. The long, sticky tentacles of this anemone vary in colour from a dull grey brown to vivid green with purple tips. The green individuals contain algae called zooxanthellae which produce food for the anemone and are also thought to remove waste products from their host. Small crabs and even a species of prawn can often be found living among its tentacles. (See pages 35 and 39.) It prefers well-lit areas down to about 20m (65ft) where it lives attached to rocks, kelp or eel grass.

Dahlia Anemone
Urticina felina

Up to 20cm (8in). This large anemone has short, thick tentacles in a variety of different colours but most often in a 'raspberry ripple' of red and cream. With all the tentacles withdrawn, it becomes an inconspicuous jelly-like mass covered in gravel and pieces of shell. It lives in areas of rock and gravel below the low water mark and feeds voraciously on prawns, young fish and other small animals.

Trumpet Anemone
Aiptasia mutabilis

Up to 12cm (8in) across. The tentacles of this anemone are a green-brown colour and it has paler streaks across the centre. It lives in rock pools and shallow water and is often found in very large numbers. The white stinging cells can often be seen coiled up inside the tips of the tentacles, as in the photograph. This is another southern species found only in the south west of the United Kingdom.

Plumose Anemone
Metridium senile

Up to 30cm (12in) high. The colour of this, the largest anemone in local waters, varies from white to grey or pale orange. It has a mass of fine tentacles which give it a distinctive fluffy appearance. It lives attached to rocks, ship-wrecks and overhangs in areas of strong current and is able to move about by sliding on its base. If any pieces of the column are torn off in this process each piece can grow into a new individual, a process of reproduction called basal laceration.

Sagartia elegans

Up to 3cm (1.2in) across. This anemone occurs in a huge variety of bright colours including red, orange, pink, brown and white, often with stripes and a contrasting centre. It lives in rock pools, caves and on vertical rock faces down to about 50m (164ft) and is often found in large groups. It can also live successfully with its column squeezed into tiny holes and crevices.

Actinothoe sphyrodeta

Up to 5cm (2in) tall. This white anemone sometimes has a pale yellow centre and can easily be confused with the white variety of Sagartia elegans (above). Unlike the latter, Actinothoe has a smooth column, often striped, with no warts and fewer, less 'tidy' tentacles. It grows in areas of strong current attached to rock faces, overhangs or, as in the photograph, on kelp stems. It can be found from the low water mark down to about 50m (164ft) and often appears in large numbers.

Cloak Anemone
Adamsia carciniopados

Up to 6cm (2.5in) tall. This anemone lives its entire life hanging upside down underneath the hermit crab *Pagurus prideauxi*. Its base wraps around the shell in which the crab is living, and is a pale yellow colour with magenta spots. The white tentacles collect any food particles dropped by the crab and, in turn, the anemone protects its host, emitting bright pink threads of stinging cells called acontia when disturbed. It also secretes a hard substance to extend the shell so that the growing crab doesn't have to move home.

Parasitic Anemone
Calliactis parasitica

Up to 10cm (4in) tall. Although it can live attached to rocks and empty shells, this anemone is most often found on the shell of the hermit crab *Pagurus bernhardus* (see page 37). It is far from parasitic and provides the crab with camouflage and protection. In return, the anemone benefits from the morsels of food scattered by the crab's untidy feeding habits. So great is the bond between crab and anemone that when the crab moves to a larger shell it takes its anemone, or often several anemones, with it. It does this by tapping a signal on its old shell and the anemone responds by loosening its grip. The crab then gently picks up the anemone and 'plants' it on the new shell.

Daisy Anemone

Cereus pedunculatus

Up to 10cm (4in) across. Despite its name, this anemone bears very little resemblance to a daisy. It is a dull grey-brown colour with lighter stripes and streaks. It lives in rock pools and shallow water and, although it often seems to be growing out of the sand, it will be attached to something solid beneath the surface. It reproduces by brooding the young inside, then releasing them through its mouth as tiny, perfectly formed individuals.

Burrowing Anemone

Peachia cylindrica

Up to 12cm (5in) across. The 12 long, tapering tentacles of this anemone are beautifully patterned with brown and cream chevrons. Some individuals, like the example in the photograph, have a white centre. It lives with its column completely buried in the seabed in areas of sand and gravel from the low water line down to at least 100m (328ft). Unlike most other anemones, it doesn't have a sucker-like disc for attaching itself to a hard surface but just a rounded end which can dig into the seabed.

Corals

Corals usually live in colonies, a mass of polyps joined together in a hard structure to form one growth, such as the Fan Coral. Soft corals, such as Deadman's Fingers, have no hard skeleton but form a flexible, gelatinous mass from which the polyps protrude. Other corals, such as the Devonshire Cup Coral, live as solitary polyps, although many individuals may live close to each other.

Corals are normally associated with the warm, clear water of the tropics but several species thrive in the waters around the Channel Islands. Although they do not produce the mass of hard skeletons that form coral reefs, they lack none of the beauty of their warm water cousins.

Deadman's Fingers
Alcyonium digitatum

Up to 25cm (10in) tall. This soft coral grows in an irregular, branching manner forming thick, blunt fingers, hence its name. The colour of the central 'body' varies from white to cream or pale orange but the polyps are always white and have eight tentacles. It feeds on plankton and grows attached to rocks in areas exposed to strong currents from the low water line down to 100m (328ft).

Red Fingers
Alcyonium glomeratum

Up to 30cm (12in) tall. This soft coral is similar to Deadman's Fingers apart from the deep orange or red of its central mass. It is also much more abundant around the Channel Islands than its paler relative and has thinner 'fingers'. Its polyps are white and can be fully retracted, leaving a lumpy, spotted mass as shown in the foreground of

the photograph. It prefers vertical rock faces and overhangs in fairly sheltered areas from 10–50m (33–164ft), and is only found in the south west of the British Isles.

Pink Soft Coral

Parerythropodium coralloides

Up to 4cm (1.5in) tall. At first glance this soft coral could be confused with small colonies of Deadman's Fingers, but its tiny size, delicate pink colour and habitat make it easy to distinguish. It grows in small cracks and crevices well out of the light and sheltered from any water movement. This is a southern species rarely found around the coasts of Britain.

Devonshire Cup Coral

Caryophyllia smithii

Up to 2cm (0.8in) across. Like all cup corals, this common species grows within a vase-shaped structure made almost entirely of calcium carbonate. Its jewel-like colours vary enormously, often with a zig zag of contrasting colour around the centre, and a transparent knob at the end of each tentacle. This is a solitary coral, growing attached to rocks from the low water line down to 100m (328ft). Close inspection may reveal the presence of a tiny barnacle, *Boscia anglica*, growing on the cup.

Sunset Coral

Leptopsammia pruvoti

Up to 4cm (1.5in) across. This rare cup coral is much larger than the Devonshire Cup Coral and has a stunning bright yellow colour. It is very slow-growing with some individuals living for over one hundred years. It reproduces very infrequently and is only very occasionally found north of the Mediterranean. In the Channel Islands it can be found on sheltered vertical walls below the kelp line, particularly around Sark.

Weymouth Carpet Coral
Hoplangia durotrix
Clusters up to 5cm (2in) across. This coral grows in clusters of tiny individuals to form a colony and has translucent brown tentacles which only emerge at night. This is another rare coral at the northernmost limit of its distribution and is only occasionally found around the coasts of the United Kingdom. Around the Channel Islands it is a little more abundant, but is easily overlooked because of its preference for living right at the back of dark crevices and caves.

Sea Fan
Eunicella verrucosa
Up to 30cm (12in) tall. The Sea Fan is usually a pale orange colour but can occasionally be pure white. It is formed of a horny substance called gorgonin which, although flexible, is very fragile and grows by just one centimetre a year. It lives attached to rocks and boulders with its fan orientated across the current so that its polyps can catch water-borne food particles. Close inspection may reveal the presence of a well-camouflaged nudibranch, *Tritonia nilsodhneri*, which feeds exclusively on this coral. (See page 48.)

3 Worms

Marine worms belong to several different animal groups but for simplicity are grouped together in one chapter. Unlike their terrestrial cousins, many of the worms found in the sea are beautiful creatures, often with colourful markings and delicate patterns.

Flatworms are the simplest of these animals, having no true body cavity and only a primitive digestive system. The segmented worms, which include all the other species described here, are much more complex with well-developed digestive, reproductive and nervous systems. Some of these, such as the Lug Worm, spend their lives crawling around or beneath the seabed while others live a sedentary life within the protection of a tube.

At low water, the beaches of the Channel Islands are littered with the spoils of worm activity but the worms themselves are hidden in the damp sand. Below the low water mark worms are much more obvious, most noticeably the tube worms with their attractive feathery tentacles.

Candy Striped Flat Worm
Prostheceraeus vittatus
Up to 5cm (2in) long. The pale yellow or cream body of this flat worm is patterned with thin, dark red stripes. It moves with an elegant rippling motion and is often found on the Light Bulb Sea Squirts (page 65) that it feeds on, as in the photograph. It can also be found under rocks and boulders around the low water line.

Sea Mouse
Aphrodite aculeata

Up to 20cm (8in) long. The Sea Mouse has a dense mat of grey-brown bristles on its back with finer, iridescent blue-green fur on its sides. It lives buried head down in muddy sand and is rarely seen above the seabed. Occasionally, when the spring tide is at its lowest, the Sea Mouse may be revealed on the beach.

Lug Worm
Arenicola marina

Up to 20cm (8in) long. This green-brown worm is extremely common in sandy areas but is very rarely seen. It lives buried in a U-shaped burrow, eating enormous quantities of sand and filtering out any organic materials for food. The worm ejects the used sand, producing the casts which are such a familiar sight above and below the water. The lug worm is popular with fishermen as bait.

Sand Mason Worm
Lanice conchilega

Tube up to 5cm (2in) tall. This segmented worm lives in a tube constructed of fragments of sand and shell. Each tube is firmly embedded in the sand or mud and has a branched top giving it the appearance of a tiny tree. It lives in shallow areas, often in huge numbers, and can be seen exposed at low water.

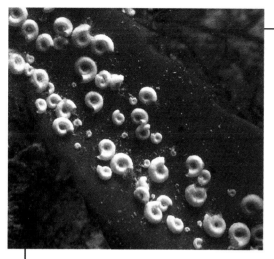

Post Horn Worm
Spirorbis sp.

Up to 0.5cm (0.2in) in diameter. The Post Horn Worm lives in a tiny, white, calcareous spiral and has bright green tentacles. It grows attached to seaweed, particularly Serrated Wrack, as well as on rock and shells including those of the Ormer. It is very common in rock pools and shallow water down to the lower edge of the kelp line.

Peacock Worm
Sabella pavonina

Tube up to 25cm (10in) long. This is the largest tube worm in local waters and its tentacles appear in a wide variety of colours, often delicately striped. Its tube is grey brown and flexible. The Peacock Worm is common in areas of sand and mud from the low water line down and often occurs in great numbers, creating a 'forest' of swaying tentacles.

Brown Tube Worm
Megalomma vesiculosum

Tentacles up to 4cm (1.5in) in diameter. This worm lives with its tube completely buried in the seabed and leaves just a round hole in the sand when it retracts its dark brown tentacles. Close inspection will reveal the presence of tiny black spheres on the ends of the tentacles. This worm lives in shallow, sandy areas sheltered from the tide.

Orange Tube Worm
Protula tubularia
Tube up to 5cm (2in) long. As its name suggests, this worm can be distinguished by its vibrant orange tentacles. It grows in a hard, white tube attached to rocks or shells in shady areas and is usually solitary. Like all tube worms, it retracts its tentacles rapidly when disturbed but, unlike many of the other species, it takes a long time to re-emerge.

Fan Worm
Bispira volutacornis
Tentacles up to 5cm (2in) in diameter. This tube worm has a beautiful double spiral of tentacles which are various shades of brown, sometimes striped with cream. It lives in a leathery grey tube and will retract very suddenly when disturbed. The Fan Worm lives between boulders and in rocky crevices, often in groups, in shallow water and the lowest rock pools.

4 Crustaceans

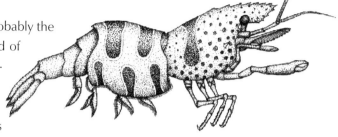

Apart from fish, crustaceans are probably the most familiar and easily-recognised of all marine creatures. They are soft-bodied animals living in a hard outer shell like a suit of armour and have jointed legs, obvious body parts and distinct eyes, often on stalks. They have well-developed sensory and nervous systems to cope with their complex lives of hunting, hiding and mating.

In order to grow, crustaceans go through the complicated process of moulting. Once the old shell is discarded, the crustacean is soft and vulnerable until the new shell has hardened up, which can take some days. Any limbs lost before the moult are regenerated on the new shell.

Many female crustaceans are only fertile just after they have moulted. This makes mating a potentially lethal procedure, although in some species the male will stay with his mate and protect her until her new shell has hardened up. The eggs are fertilised by the male, then carried for several months by the female in a specially-developed flap beneath her abdomen. They hatch as tiny planktonic young, developing into the adult form when they take up their life on the seabed.

For centuries the fishing industry in the Channel Islands has depended heavily on the plentiful supply of crustaceans. Shrimps used to be gathered by hand in the larger sandy bays, a tradition that has now just about died out. Fishing for Lobsters and crabs, however, is still big business. Originally the pots were made of willow and were raised and lowered manually and, being fairly fragile, were only used in the summer. With the development of tough steel and plastic pots and mechanical winches, fishing for Lobsters and crabs is now a year-round business with some boats able to fish 1000 pots a day. More restrictions are being imposed on the fishing industry to protect the stocks. Even so, the tonnage of Lobster taken from the waters around the Channel Islands amounts to more than half that taken from around the coasts of England and Wales put together. Such numbers might seem unsustainable but local waters are amongst the richest in the world in this particular species.

Common Prawn
Palaemon serratus
Up to 5cm (2in) long. This is the prawn so often found hiding under the seaweed in rock pools. It is almost transparent with delicate brown and yellow spots and stripes. It is also found hiding in crevices in rocky areas down to  about 40m (130ft) and often seems to share its home quite happily with crabs and blennies. Like all prawns, it is rarely still and seems to 'dance' constantly.

Anemone Prawn
Periclimenes sagittifer
Up to 3cm (1.2in) long. The transparent body of this prawn is marked with beautiful lilac stripes and chevrons. Its legs have similar violet bands and there are tiny brown spots on its head. It seems to live exclusively within the tentacles of the Snakelocks Anemone (see page 22) although the exact relationship with its host is not known. This prawn was first described in St Catherine's Bay, Jersey, in 1861. There are still no British records outside the Channel Islands.

Lobster
Homarus gammarus

Up to 75cm (29.5in) long. The bright-blue colour of the Lobster's thick shell makes it impossible to confuse with any other species. Its larger claw is used for crushing while the lighter claw is a narrower cutting tool. It lives a solitary life in rocky areas and on shipwrecks, emerging from its hole only at night to feed. This important commercial species and well-known cannibal can live for over 60 years if it manages to avoid the danger of the lobster pot.

Crawfish or Spiny Lobster
Palinurus elephas

Up to 60cm (24in) long. As the alternative common name of the Crawfish suggests, its orangey-red carapace is covered in small spines. It uses its long, rough antennae like whips to defend itself, having no large claws like a Lobster or crab. It can be found on rocky ledges below 20m (65ft) in the summer but lives in much deeper water for the rest of the year. The Crawfish, or 'squeaker' as it is known locally, was once abundant in the waters around the Channel Islands but, due to over-fishing, is now a very rare sight.

Hermit Crab
Pagurus bernhardus

Carapace up to 4cm (1.5in). Young Hermit Crabs can be found in a variety of different shells but the largest are nearly always in whelk shells, often accompanied by one or more 'parasitic' anemones. (See page 25.) Changing shell is done

with much caution and speed so that the soft, vulnerable tail is exposed for the shortest time possible. This very common crab can be found at all depths on most types of seabed. Hermit crabs with slender claws with some purple markings may be a different species, *Pagurus prideauxi*. (See page 25.)

Squat Lobster
Galathea squamifera

Up to 6.5cm (2.5in) long. The shell of this Squat Lobster is a chestnut brown or olive green colour with intricate stripes on the carapace. Its flattened body is the perfect shape

for its life in holes and crevices, into which it withdraws very rapidly when disturbed. This is a shy creature, very rarely seen out in the open. Larger individuals with bright blue markings are likely to be the Spiny Squat Lobster, *Galathea strigosa* (right).

Broad-clawed Porcelain Crab

Porcellana platycheles

Carapace up to 1.5cm (0.6in) across. This tiny grey-brown crab is covered with bristly hairs. As its name suggests, it has very broad, flattened claws and its carapace is also flattened, making it perfectly adapted for its

life under stones and rocks. Its fifth pair of legs is very tiny and often tucked under the body out of sight. It can be found in rock pools, under stones and in shallow water down to about 15m (49ft).

Teddy Bear Crab *Dromia personata*

Carapace up to 8cm (3in) across. This crab is also known as the Sponge Crab as it is often entirely covered with sponge. It is a red-brown colour with bright pink, glossy claws and a covering of soft, velvety hair giving it a furry appearance. It lives in rocky areas and, although it can be seen around the low water mark, it is more common at about 30m (98ft).

Scorpion Spider Crab
Inachus sp.
Carapace up to 2cm (0.8in) long. This small crab has a triangular carapace and long slender legs. It often holds its claws folded under the body as in the photograph. It covers itself in tiny pieces of sponge and seaweed to provide camouflage in the stony, rocky areas it prefers. It can also be found living in the tentacles of the Snakelocks Anemone. The exact relationship with the anemone is not known but it is thought that the Scorpion Spider Crab feeds off the tentacles themselves.

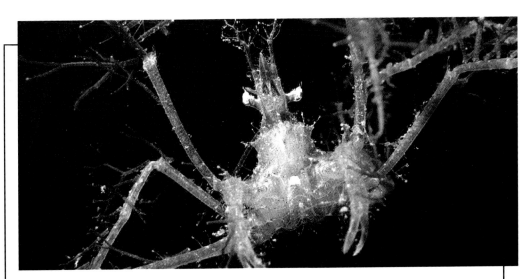

Slender Spider Crab *Macropodia tenuirostris*
Carapace up to 2cm (0.8in) across. This tiny crab can be incredibly difficult to spot as it often camouflages itself by planting leafy red seaweeds on its back and legs. It has a triangular carapace and very long, thin legs and pincers. It is a pale, greeny-yellow colour and has an elongated 'nose'. It lives in shallow water on a variety of seabeds, but particularly amongst seaweed.

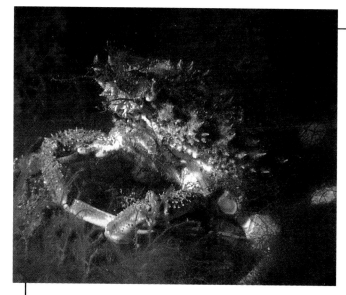

Spiny Spider Crab
Maja squinado

Carapace up to 20cm (8in) across. The domed, circular carapace of this crab is rather small in comparison to its very long, slender legs. Its spiny back is often covered with a garden of sponge and seaweed which the crab plants there for camouflage and which it carefully transfers to its new shell after moulting. It lives on sand and amongst rocks down to about 50m (165ft) but comes inshore in large numbers in the summer to moult and mate, forming huge writhing mounds of crabs and empty shells as it does so. This is another commercially-important species.

Masked Crab
Corystes cassivelaunus

Carapace up to 5cm (2in) long. Although fairly common, this little crab is very rarely seen in the day time as it spends most of its life buried in the sand. Its long antennae fuse together to form a tube, rather like a snorkel, so that it can draw clean, oxygenated water down below the seabed. If disturbed, it will re-bury itself astonishingly quickly, slipping backwards into the sand as in the photograph. It lives in sand and silty areas at all depths.

Edible Crab
Cancer pagurus

Carapace up to 30cm (12in) across. The thick shell of this crab is a pinky-brown colour with darker markings on the claws and distinctive crimped edges to the carapace. It lives in cracks and beneath boulders in rocky areas or buried in the seabed in sandy or shingle habitats. Young Edible Crabs can be found in rock pools and shallow water, with older individuals living as deep as 100m (330ft). This important commercial species can live for up to 20 years and is known locally as a chancre crab.

Velvet Swimming Crab *Necora puber*

Carapace up to 10cm (4in) across. This common crab, with its iridescent purple markings and bright red eyes, is extremely aggressive, threatening even the largest intruder with waving arms and snapping claws. It lives in rock pools and deeper water in kelpy, rocky areas. In the photograph, the larger male is guarding the female beneath him from other suitors until she sheds her shell and he is able to mate with her. This is known locally as the lady crab.

Shore Crab

Carcinus maenas

Carapace up to 8cm (3in) across. The colour of this very common crab varies from olive green to brown or grey. It is able to live in almost any marine habitat but is most often found in rock pools and areas of sand, rock or seaweed down to over 70m (230ft) When threatened it can

quickly bury itself in the sand. The Shore Crab in the photograph is a female 'in berry', carrying her eggs in a flap on her belly.

Hairy Crab

Pilumnus hirtellus

Carapace up to 2cm (0.8in) across. This small crab is a red-brown colour with some lighter patches on its claws. It is covered in rough hair which is thickest on the legs. Its claws are relatively large with one bigger than the other, a feature

of many crabs. It lives under stones, in cracks and on sponges in rocky areas from the low water mark down to about 70m (230ft).

5 Molluscs

The animals in this group appear to be so different from each other that it's difficult to imagine that they are related at all. What does a Scallop have in common with a Squid and in what way is a Dog Whelk like a sea slug? The one thing they all have in common is a soft body. Indeed the word 'mollusc' is derived from the Latin 'mollis' which means soft. Many have an external shell, some even have two, while others have an internal shell and some have no shell at all. Whatever their differences, molluscs are an incredibly successful group of animals and are found on all types of seabed in some form or other.

Gastropods
Molluscs with one shell

Most of the animals in this section of the mollusc group, which includes limpets, Ormers and sea snails, have shells. This grows with its owner so there is no need for the moulting process that crustaceans have to go through. Gastropods move around by sliding their muscular foot along a specially secreted trail of mucus. Even limpets, which seem to be static, move about the rocks in search of food returning later to exactly the same 'home' position by retracing this trail.

The best known representative of this group of animals in the Channel Islands must be the Ormer (page 44) which has been gathered at low water for centuries. Razorfish, winkles, limpets and many other shellfish were also collected, particularly during the German occupation of the Second World War, but now only the Common Whelk is fished commercially. Shell Beach on Herm is perhaps the best place to see empty gastropod shells but many varieties can be found washed up on all the Islands' beaches.

Ormer
Haliotis tuberculata

Up to 12cm (5in) long. Ormers are found in shallow water underneath weed-covered rocks and boulders. For centuries they have been gathered by hand on the lowest spring tides, known locally as ormering tides, and are considered a real delicacy in the Islands. Many gardens and walls are still decorated with the empty mother-of-pearl lined shells, once exported by the tonne for inlay work in the furniture industry. Stern fishing regulations now restrict the times when these shellfish can be gathered in order to protect the stocks. The Channel Islands represent the northerly extent of the Ormer which is not found around the coast of mainland Britain.

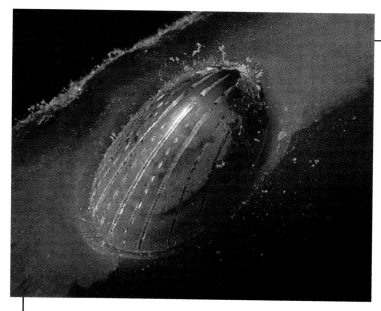

Blue-rayed Limpet
Helcion pellucidum

Up to 2cm (0.8in). The Blue-rayed Limpet has a delicate, almost translucent, shell with beautiful iridescent blue stripes. This tiny limpet feeds by scraping off the surface of the kelp on which it lives and at the same time hollows out a home for itself on the stipe or blade of the seaweed. The hollows eaten into the stipe can cause it to be so weakened that the whole plant is swept away.

Painted Topshell
Calliostoma zizyphinum

Up to 3cm (1.2in). This species is mostly found in rocky areas at all depths where it grazes on algae and tiny organisms. It has a pale, distinctly steep-sided cone with very colourful purple or crimson markings that the animal is thought to clean by rubbing its foot over the shell.

Slipper Limpet
Crepidula fornicata

Up to 5cm (2in) long. This is not a native species but is thought to have come from North America in water carried as ship's ballast. It now thrives all around the Channel Islands and along the south coast of Britain, and in some areas occurs in such high density that it is considered a pest. Slipper Limpets are found in fairly shallow water attached to Scallops and oysters or in mating chains of up to 12 individuals. In these chains, the female is on the bottom, a male is on the top and those in between are in a confused transitional stage from male to female.

European Cowrie
Trivia monacha
Up to 1.5cm (0.6in) long. The European Cowrie has a pale, ridged shell marked with three conspicuous dark spots. When the animal is alive, this beautiful shell is almost completely covered by the dappled mantle that extends from beneath the shell. This cowrie is commonly found in rocky areas and on the Colonial Sea Squirts that it eats, but is often overlooked because of its small size.

Dogwhelk
Nucella lapillus
Up to 3cm (1.2in) long. The Dogwhelk occurs in various colours from pale grey or cream to shades of brown and often has stripes, like the example in the photograph. This is a scavenger feeding on dead animals which it can 'smell' from a distance through its long siphon. Dogwhelks are widespread on rocky shores and amongst barnacles on which they also prey.

Common Whelk
Buccinum undatum
Up to 11cm (4.3in). These large shellfish are found on shingle and sandy seabeds at

all depths and are scavengers, feeding on dead animal matter. Their empty shells are often 'recycled' into homes by Hermit Crabs. (See page 37.) Many tonnes are caught locally, processed and exported to the Far East where they are considered a delicacy, making whelk fishing an important new source of fisheries revenue for the Channel Islands. The whelk's pale yellow egg mass (above left), which is about the size of an apple, is often washed up on the shore and contains tiny, perfectly-formed baby whelks.

Seahare *Aplysia punctata*
Up to 30cm (12in) long. These large sea-slugs have a very fragile, internal shell. They are often seen in spring and early summer grazing in shallow water on sea lettuce. Their coloration varies from a rich red-brown to olive green or even black and they usually have lighter-coloured speckles. When disturbed they will eject a purple ink. Seahares are hermaphrodites and often mate in chains, each one being fertilized by the one above it while fertilizing the one below.

Nudibranchs
Molluscs with no shell

Sea slugs, or 'nudibranchs' to give them their correct title, are some of the most colourful creatures in the sea but they are easy to overlook because they are so small. The name 'nudibranch' literally means 'naked gill' and refers to their conspicuous exposed gills which appear as either a feathery circle on the rear or tentacle-like projections all over the body.

Most nudibranchs are carnivorous, feeding on sponges, hydroids and sea squirts. As most of these live below the low water mark it is uncommon to find nudibranchs in rock pools, making diving the easiest way to see these beautiful creatures. Look for the animals they feed on and the conspicuous ribbons and coils of their egg masses, and the nudibranch should be close by. The steep underwater rock faces around Sark are probably the best places to find them in the Channel Islands, especially in the early summer when the nudibranchs are busy reproducing.

Tritonia nilsodhneri

Up to 3.5cm (1.4in). The salmon-pink colour of this nudibranch and the 'tassels' down its back allow it to blend almost imperceptibly with the Fan Coral on which it lives and feeds. This species also occurs in a pure white form, presumably so that it can be camouflaged on the White Fan corals. The photograph shows two individuals coiled around a branch of the coral with a ribbon of spawn behind them.

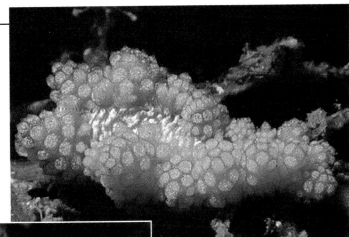

Doto fragilis

Up to 3cm (1.2in). The pale brown body of this nudibranch is covered with two rows of tentacles which look like tiny bunches of grapes. It feeds on hydroids such as the *Halecium halecinum* in the

photograph and *Nemertesia*. (See page 17.) Its wavy lines of white spawn (left) can often be seen on these hydroids indicating the presence of the less conspicuous adults.

Diaphorodoris luteocincta

Up to 1cm (0.4in). The Latin name for this nudibranch literally translates as 'diaphanous, yellow-ringed sea nymph' which is rather a grand title for such a tiny creature. Its small size and conspicuous central red blotch make it difficult to confuse with any other species. It prefers rocky areas with silt where it feeds on bryozoans.

Acanthodoris pilosa
Up to 5cm (2in). This nudibranch is easy to distinguish from others by its large circle of gills and 'fluffy' appearance. Its colour can vary from pale cream or white to brown and black. The individual in the photograph is

feeding on one of its favourite bryozoans, *Alcyonidium diaphanun* (see page 56), and to the left is a ribbon of its egg spawn.

Polycera faeroensis
Up to 4.5cm (1.8in). This is one of the most common nudibranchs in the Channel Islands and perhaps the easiest to spot. The translucent white body has yellow markings on the tips of the gills and the tentacles around the mouth. It can also have yellow stripes on its tail and spots on its body. The photograph shows two individuals in the head-to-toe mating position common to all nudibranchs, joined by their reproductive organs.

Thecacera pennigera

Up to 3cm (1.2in). The pale body of this species is adorned with beautiful orange and black spots and a conspicuous frill of gills. It feeds on the bryozoan *Bugula plumosa* (see page 58) on which it also lays its untidy white ribbons of spawn. This is another southern species which also occurs in the Mediterranean.

Cadlina laevis

Up to 3cm (1.2in). This nudibranch is white and covered with tiny warty projections. In some individuals, these projections are a pale yellow colour and there is a yellow rim around the edge of the mantle, like the animal illustrated. Its gill circle is quite small and can be fully retracted. It feeds on sponges such as *Hemimycale columella*, as shown in the photograph.

Doris sticta

Up to 4.5cm (1.8in). The distinctive irregular projections on this species are called tubercles. They give it an appearance quite unlike any other common local species. It is pale yellow with the tips of the tubercles coloured purple or dark brown. This is a southern species also found in the Mediterranean and is thought to feed on sponges.

Sea Lemon

Archidoris pseudoargus

Up to 12cm (5in). The body of this, one of the largest nudibranchs, is a pale yellow colour mottled with various

shades of brown, pink or green. It has a warty texture with a very conspicuous gill circle. It feeds on sponges in rocky areas below the low water mark but in the spring it moves into shallower water to spawn and so can sometimes be found in rock pools. The wide ribbon of spawn is laid in a spiral as shown in the photograph (left).

Coryphella browni

Up to 5cm (2in). The translucent body of this species is covered with crimson tassels, called cerata, with white tips. It feeds on hydroids, mainly *Tubularia indivisa* (see page 17), and is able to eat the stinging cells of its host without harm. These cells are then manoeuvered to the end of the nudibranch's cerata to create its own defence system.

Bivalves
Molluscs with two shells

The soft body of some molluscs is protected inside two shells hinged together. These are known as bivalves and include mussels, oysters and scallops. Although some of them can swim, they live a sedentary life, relying on the current to bring them particles of food which they filter through their gills. Light-sensitive structures around the edge of the shell allow them to detect movement and clamp the shell firmly shut if danger threatens.

Scallops, the largest bivalves in the Channel Islands, are collected commercially by divers and by dredging. Some areas of the seabed are farmed, with young Scallops, known as spat, planted to replace the adults removed. In the 19th century thousands of tonnes of the native oyster were gathered and exported every year. At its peak hundreds of men, women and children were employed in the industry gathering, sorting and packing these delicacies.

Portuguese Oyster
Crassostrea gigas

Up to 15cm (6in) long. The Portuguese Oyster was originally introduced as a commercially-farmed species but is now more successful than the native Flat Oyster. It grows in shallow water, often with one half of the shell fused to the rocks or stones. Oysters are still farmed in Jersey, Guernsey and Herm although in smaller quantities than in the past.

Scallop
Pecten maximus

Up to 15cm (6in) wide. The scallop's natural enemy is the Spiny Starfish (see page 61), which it can 'smell' at a distance through the sensory tentacles around the edge of its mantle. It can escape by swimming away, expelling water to propel itself by opening and clamping its two shells together. It is found in tide-swept areas of sand and shingle below the low water mark.

Cephalopods
Molluscs with an internal shell

The cephalopods, that is Cuttlefish, Octopus and Squid, are the most highly developed of the molluscs and have the largest brains of all the invertebrates. They also have an incredible facility to change the colour of their skin by expanding and contracting special pigment cells called chromatophores. When disturbed, they discharge a cloud of ink which confuses potential predators and may even act as an anaesthetic. Other characteristics of this group are the jet propulsion system (for extremely fast getaways), and the internal shell which controls the animal's buoyancy by adjusting the amount of gas it contains.

Until the extremely cold winter of 1962–63 the Octopus was abundant all around the Channel Islands but is now rarely seen. Cuttlefish and Squid, however, are still fairly common and are most often seen inshore in the summer months.

Cuttlefish *Sepia officinalis*

Up to 40cm (16in). The Cuttlefish has an amazing ability to change its texture and colour instantly to blend almost imperceptibly with the terrain. During courtship and hunting it can flash vivid stripes and patterns across its body. It is a voracious predator, taking crabs and fish almost as large as itself. When disturbed, it is able to 'jet' away rapidly, leaving a large cloud of ink behind. The internal shell is commonly seen washed up on the beach. During the occupation of the islands by the German forces in the Second World War, Cuttlefish shells were powdered and used as toothpaste.

Little Cuttle
Sepiola atlantica

Up to 5cm (2in). This tiny creature is often mistaken for a juvenile Cuttlefish but is a separate species easily distinguished from its larger cousin by the proportionally much larger eyes as well as its smaller overall size. The Little Cuttle spends most of the daytime buried in the sand with just its eyes protruding watching for prey. When disturbed it will emit perfect little rings of ink. It is most likely to be encountered by divers at night, when it is much more active.

Squid
Alloteuthis subulata

Up to 21cm (8.3in). The Squid is much more elongated than the Cuttlefish and tends to spend its time in the water column rather than resting on the seabed. Its translucent body is covered with deep red speckles and it will squirt ink when distressed. This small species of Squid is seen inshore in the summer and is often attracted to bright lights at night.

6 Bryozoans

Bryozoans are among the most common animals of the rocky shore, often covering large areas, but are easily overlooked because of their relatively small size. Each bryozoan is a colony of hundreds of tiny animals, each less than a millimetre across, living inside a tough rectangular box. Each animal captures food particles from the water, using retractable tentacles. Their growth forms vary from encrusting mats and bushy tufts to gelatinous lobes and hard, brittle uprights. Bryozoans are mostly hermaphrodites and can reproduce sexually to create free-swimming larvae which spend some time in the plankton. If the larva finds a favourable place to settle, it can then rapidly create a whole new colony by budding fresh individuals.

As well as forming a substantial part of the animal undergrowth, or turf, bryozoans are also an important food source, especially for nudibranchs. There are many species around the Channel Islands, the seven illustrated being the most common.

Alcyonidium diaphanum

Up to 20cm (8in). This species forms soft, gelatinous branching fingers with a smooth surface covered in tiny hairs. It is a pale brown colour and grows below the low water mark in current-swept areas of mixed seabed and on shipwrecks. It is thought that an itchy, allergic reaction occurs if one of these comes into contact with human skin.

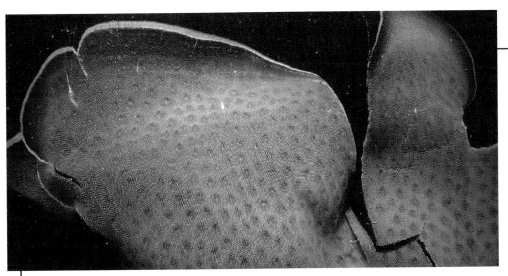

Sea Mat *Membranipora membranacea*

This very common encrusting bryozoan grows rapidly on the blades of kelp, forming a pale, lacy pattern across the surface of the seaweed. Even with the naked eye it is possible to see the tiny boxes holding the individuals that make up the colony.

Cellaria fistulosa

Up to 10cm (4in) high. The ivory-coloured colonies of this species are branched and it is brittle and hard to the touch. It grows on rock faces, boulders and shipwrecks in areas with some current below 15m (50ft) and can form large growths.

Hornwrack
Flustra foliacea

Up to 20cm (8in). This species forms branching, leaf-like colonies that are crisp but flexible. It is a pale brown colour and grows in rocky areas with strong currents and often covers large areas of seabed. When rubbed, it produces a strong lemon smell and some local fishermen use it to remove the odour of fish from their hands.

Bugula plumosa

Up to 5cm (2in). The delicate, feathery spirals of this bryozoan are a pale buff colour and resemble tiny fir trees. It grows in small patches attached to rocks below the water mark and seems to prefer overhangs.

Bugula flabellata

Up to 5cm (2in) high. This bryozoan forms delicate, pale orange leafy spirals with fringed edges. It has a crisp texture and grows below the low water line on any hard surface, often attached to other bryozoans.

Ross or Rose Coral **Pentapora foliacea**

Up to 1m (3.3ft) across. The common name for this species is misleading as it is definitely not a coral, although its stony growth resembles hard coral in that it is very brittle and fragile. The dome-shaped orange-brown colonies provide a home for many other animals which hide in its folds. It grows on stony ground well below the low water line in areas exposed to some current.

7 Echinoderms

'Echinoderm' literally means 'spiny skin', a characteristic found to some extent in all of the animals in this group. Another distinctive feature is their five-rayed symmetry, most obviously illustrated in the starfish. The other animals in this group are urchins, sea cucumbers, feather stars and brittle stars.

Echinoderms have an unusual method of propulsion, a hydraulic system unique to this group of animals. It takes the form of hollow tentacles known as 'tube feet' which the animal can extend or retract by varying the water pressure inside them. Tiny suckers on the end provide grip, allowing the creature to move across vertical or even overhanging surfaces.

Sea urchins have another unique feature in the form of their complex mouth, called 'Aristotle's lantern'. It is made up of five chisel-like teeth that work together to produce an extremely powerful chewing and scraping device.

Sea cucumbers seem to bear little resemblance to starfish and urchins but do share their basic five-rayed symmetry. Some are free ranging, using their tube feet to move around the seabed in search of food. Others live sedentary lives buried in the gravel or wedged in a crevice and have developed their tube feet into tentacles for catching food. The sedentary type is more common in the Channel Islands.

Although the small Cushion Starfish and Shore Urchin can be found in rock pools around the islands, the best place to see echinoderms is well below the low water line on rocky reefs and walls. This is the ideal grazing area for the colourful Common Urchin and Bloody Henry Starfish as well as the larger Spiny Starfish and the Sunstar. The Common Starfish, which is so numerous on the northern side of the Channel, is very rarely seen around the Islands.

Bloody Henry Starfish
Henricia oculata
Up to 12cm (5in). These starfish occur in a variety of beautiful colours from vivid scarlet to purple, mauve and brown, with a paler shade on the underside. They are fairly common around the Channel Islands, preferring rocky areas and kelp forests below the low water line where they browse on sponges. Like all starfish, the Bloody Henry can easily regenerate an arm if one is lost or damaged.

Spiny Starfish
Marthasterias glacialis
Up to 70cm. The large size and spine-covered arms of this starfish make it difficult to confuse with any other species in local waters. Its arms are soft and floppy and often tinged with purple towards the tips. The Spiny Starfish is a voracious predator and feeds mainly on bivalves which it prises open using its tube feet. The starfish then extends its stomach between the two shells to eat its prey. Such behaviour has made this starfish particularly unpopular with scallop divers.

Sunstar
Crossaster papposus

Up to 34cm (13in). The Sunstar is easy to distinguish from other starfish by its number of arms, usually between 8 and 13. It has a large, red central disc and vivid orange arms with striking white bands. The Sunstar preys on other starfish, even other Sunstars, but is not very common in the Channel Islands. It can occasionally be seen in rocky, tide-swept areas below the low water line.

Cushion Star
Asterina gibbosa

Up to 5cm (2in). The Cushion Star has five short blunt arms and ranges in colour from olive green to brown. It lives in rocky areas at all depths and can often be found clinging to the underside of pebbles in rock pools. Unlike other starfish it begins its life as a male and then changes into a fully functional female four years later.

Black Brittle Star
Ophiocomina nigra
Up to 28cm (11in). This species is dark brown or black in colour with 5–7 arms fringed with paler bristles. It lives in open areas on sand, gravel or bedrock and can form dense beds with over 100 animals in a square metre. Off the south-west corner of Jersey there is a large bed of these Brittle Stars which completely covers any lobster pots placed in the area.

Common or Edible Urchin
Echinus esculentus
Up to 16cm (6.3in). This is the largest urchin in local waters and appears in pale shades of pink, mauve and green. It feeds by 'grazing' on algae and tiny encrusting animals in rocky regions where it plays an important role in maintaining the diversity of the area. The pattern of five sections of which all animals in this group are composed is clearly visible in the stripes of colour radiating from the centre of the urchin.

Shore or Green Urchin

Psammechinus miliaris

Up to 5cm (2in). This tiny urchin lives at all depths but is most often encountered under stones in rock pools. It is particularly fond of areas with encrusting pink algae, as shown in the photograph, and can cover itself in pieces of

weed and shell for camouflage. The Shore Urchin is a rapacious predator, feeding on seaweeds, barnacles, sea squirts and molluscs.

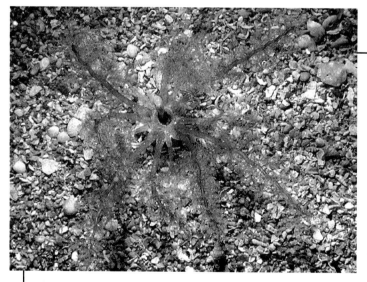

Gravel Cucumber

Neopentadactyla mixta

Tentacles up to 10cm (4in). As its name suggests, this cucumber occurs in areas of gravel and shingle and lives with its body buried beneath the surface of the seabed. The pale, mucus-covered tentacles trap food particles which are then passed to the central mouth. If disturbed these tentacles will withdraw rapidly and may remain out of sight for several hours. A cucumber with darker tentacles found growing in cracks in the rocks is likely to be the Brown Cucumber, *Aslia lefevrei*.

8 Sea Squirts

Sea squirts are extremely common animals found at all depths, even in rock pools but, because of their small size and apparent lack of movement, they are often overlooked. They appear in a huge variety of colours, many of them very vibrant, and grow in a range of different shapes. Some form erect tubes or spheres while others grow in encrusting mats which can easily be mistaken for sponges.

All sea squirts are basically cylindrical, jelly-like bodies with two openings called siphons. One siphon draws water into the animal's body, where it filters out the food particles it needs, passing them through its intestine for processing. The used water is then exhaled through the second opening.

Young sea squirts begin life in a larval form, rather like a tadpole, and have a simple backbone and nerve cord. Although this is lost when the larvae settle down and develop into the adult form, it is an indication of the complexity of this apparently simple animal.

Sea squirts live either as individuals or fused together to form colonies. They attach themselves to a variety of surfaces and can survive in areas of low salinity or even in polluted water. When a squirt is disturbed, it quickly contracts its body, causing the water inside to squirt out, hence its common name.

Light Bulb Sea Squirt
Clavelina lepadiformis
Up to 2cm (0.8in) long. This squirt grows in the form of a series of transparent tubes attached at the base to form a colony of up to 300 individuals. Each one has two cream or white lines running along its

length and forming conspicuous rings around the siphon, giving the appearance of a light bulb element, hence the common name given to this species.

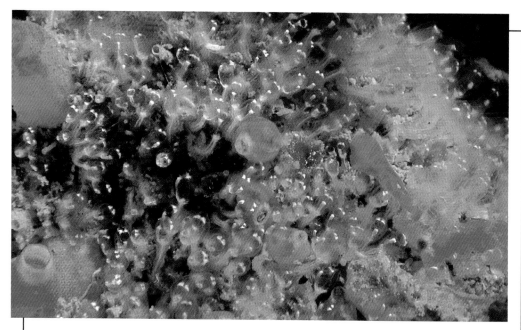

Neon Sea Squirt *Pycnoclavella aurilucens*

Up to 0.6cm (0.2in) tall. The tiny size of this sea squirt makes it very easy to overlook. It forms transparent cylinders joined at the base and has three bright orange or cream markings on the other end. It grows on vertical rock faces in areas with plenty of water movement from the kelp zone down to about 30m (100ft).

Morchellium argus

Up to 3cm (1.2in) in diameter. Each of the spheres formed by this species is actually many individuals fused together to create a colony. A red stalk attaches it to the rock surface, usually in small clusters on vertical faces or overhangs. It prefers areas with some water movement and lives from the low water line down to about 30m (100ft).

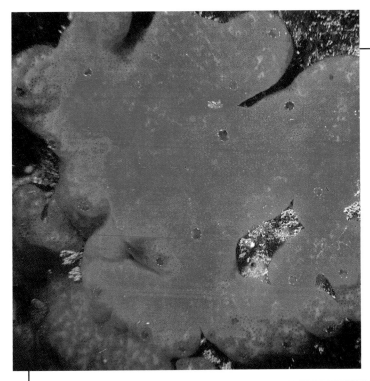

Red Sea Squirt
Polysyncraton lacazei

Up to 30cm (12in) across. This sea squirt forms bulbous cushions covered in a pattern of tiny holes with a few larger openings. It can occur in bright blood red as well as pink, yellow or blue and grows on vertical rocky surfaces. It is a southern species rarely occurring further north than the English Channel.

Jelly Sea squirt *Diplosoma spongiforme*

Up to 30cm (12in) across. This species forms extensive, transparent sheets and has a blue or white tinge. Its irregular surface is covered in masses of tiny inhalant holes with fewer, larger exhalant pores. It grows on rock and other hard surfaces and is easily mistaken for a sponge.

Yellow Sea Squirt
Ciona intestinalis

Up to 12cm (5in) long. This squirt forms a soft, gelatinous cylinder with two openings. It is almost transparent with a pale yellow or orange colour and bright yellow markings around the scalloped edges of the siphons. It can grow in sheltered or exposed areas and thrives on man-made structures. It is particularly abundant in the islands' harbours and marinas. In this photograph it can be seen growing with *Ascidiella aspersa* and *Styela clava*.

Asicidia mentula

Up to 10cm (4in) long. The oval cylinder of this sea squirt has one siphon at the top and another one half way down, both with scalloped edges. It is pinky-red in colour with white markings around the openings and feels much more solid than other

squirts. It is found in clumps on wrecks and vertical rock faces but is often covered with silt and therefore easily overlooked.

Gooseberry Sea Squirt *Dendrodoa grossularia*

Up to 2.5cm (1in) in diameter. The Gooseberry Sea Squirt is bright red, despite its name, and forms individual spheres with two openings on the top. It lives in a wide range of habitats from sheltered areas to very exposed surge gullies and can occur in large numbers. It often lives in association with a creamy white sponge called *Clathrina coriacea*.

Lesser Gooseberry Sea Squirt

Distomus variolosus

Up to 1cm (0.4in) in diameter. This bright, shiny red sea squirt is rounded and has two openings on the top. It grows fused to other individuals in dense colonies on rock and kelp stems, preferring areas exposed to the currents. It is often confused with the Gooseberry Sea Squirt which is larger and grows as separate spheres.

Stolonica socialis

Up to 1.5cm (0.6in) in diameter. This pale yellow or orange sea squirt forms oval spheres with two distinct openings on the top. Each individual is joined to its neighbour at the base, forming a colony which can cover fairly large areas. It is often confused with the Gooseberry Sea Squirt which is a darker colour, more rounded and less common in the Channel Islands.

Star Squirt
Botryllus schlosseri

Up to 10cm (4in) across. The Star Sea Squirt is a colonial species with several individuals joining together like petals forming a flower. Its colours are incredibly varied and include many shades of yellow, green, purple and blue, always with a dark spot in the centre of each colony. It encrusts rocks, wrecks and the stems of kelp from the low water line down to about 20m (65ft).

9 Fishes

Biologically, the majority of fishes are divided into two groups: those with cartilaginous skeletons, such as sharks and rays, and those with a bony skeleton, which includes all the other species. Although all fish have the same basic components of fins, tail, eyes and mouth, the different families have developed dramatically varied shapes, colours and patterns to suit their lifestyles and habitats. The flattened shape and mottled colours of the Sole, for example, make it perfectly adapted to its life on the seabed while the silvery colour and streamlined shape of the Bass make it an ideal open water fish.

All fishes have an amazing ability to detect tiny changes in water pressure through a series of sensors along their side called the lateral line. It enables them to find their way in the dark without bumping into each other or the seabed and helps them catch their food, aided by their acute sense of smell.

When it comes to courtship and reproduction, fishes also show great diversity. All are either male or female although some may change from one to the other part way through their life. Some have elaborate courtship rituals which can involve nest-building or changing colour to attract a mate. While all fishes lay eggs, the amount of parental care also varies enormously. Open water fishes tend to release huge quantities of eggs into the water and trust that a few will survive to adulthood. Seahorses take things to the other extreme with the male nurturing the eggs in his pouch until they develop into fully-formed individuals.

The waters of the Channel Islands contain a great variety of fishes, some of which are resident all year round, while others are summer visitors from further south. In the winter most fishes move to deeper, warmer offshore waters, avoiding the rapid temperature changes and stormy nature of the shallows. In the spring they return inshore to spawn and, by the summer, the rock pools, sandy bays and kelpy reefs are teeming with fish.

Lesser Spotted Dog Fish
Scyliorhinus canicula

Up to 1m (3.3ft). This is the most common member of the shark family to be found in local waters. Its sandy colours and darker spots help it to blend with the sand, gravel and rocky seabed it prefers. In the summer, the

female moves into the weedy shallows to lay her egg case, known as a mermaid's purse (left), which hatches 8–10 months later. The skin of the Dog Fish is covered in tiny spines, making it extremely rough, so much so that it was once used as sandpaper. This species is sold in the local fish markets as rock salmon.

Marbled Electric Ray
Torpedo mamorata

Up to 60cm (24in). The Marbled Electric Ray has a very rounded shape, making it easy to distinguish from other rays. It has smooth, brown skin patterned with a darker 'marbling' and a much paler underside. This nocturnal fish lies buried in the sand by day. Its electricity is generated in organs in the wings which can produce shocks up to an incredible 220 volts at 8 amps. This is enough to stun a grown man and has been known to shock a fisherman before he has even been aware of his catch!

Thornback Ray
Raja clavata
Up to 1m (3.3ft). The Thornback Ray, or Roker, is one of the most commonly-encountered rays in Channel Island waters. It has a pointed nose and wing tips and a mottled grey-brown colouring with pale spots in the centre of each wing. As its name suggests, it has rows of thorn-shaped spines along its back and down the tail. This ray is found at all depths in areas of sand and gravel and lays an egg sack, or mermaid's purse, from which the young emerge 4–5 months later.

Undulate Ray
Raja undulata
Up to 1m (3.3ft). This ray has the same pointed shape as the Thornback but is distinguished by its beautiful markings of spots and wavy lines in shades of grey and brown. It lives in sandy areas, spending most of the year in fairly deep water, below 45m (148ft), and coming closer inshore in the autumn to mate. It lays dark red egg capsules, about 9cm (3.5in) long, which have a long horn at each corner. Both the British shore and boat-caught records for this fish are held in the Channel Islands.

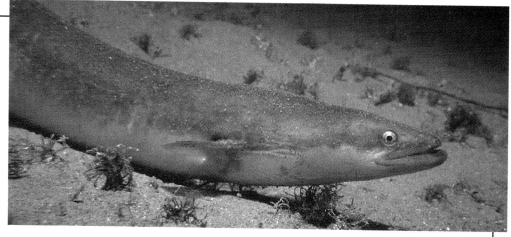

Common Eel *Anguilla anguilla*

Males up to 50cm (20in), females up to 1m (3.3ft). The Common Eel is a brown-grey colour with paler undersides and a lower jaw longer than the upper. This helps to distinguish it from its much larger relative, the Conger Eel, as does the dorsal fin which starts much further back than the Conger's. It can be found in shallow kelpy areas and sometimes lurks in the weedy corners of rock pools. This eel spends much of its life in fresh water and has even been found in the local sewage works!

Conger Eel

Conger conger

Up to 3m (10ft). This large, blue-grey eel never enters fresh water and prefers the shelter of rocky caves and shipwrecks which it leaves at night to hunt. Despite its vicious reputation, the Conger can be closely approached underwater and will only become aggressive if it feels threatened. In the Middle Ages, huge quantities of Conger were caught and exported, a Channel Island industry described in the Doomsday Book. Until recent times, fishermen used to sell Congers from door to door in barrows, a tradition now lost with the diminishing popularity of recipes such as conger and marigold soup.

Pouting *Trisopterus luscus*

Up to 60cm (24in). This beautiful copper-coloured fish has three or four vertical silver stripes, although these can be very indistinct, and a characteristic single chin barbel. Shoals of Pouting cloak many of the Islands' wrecks with the largest individuals skulking inside the darkest holes. Young fish form smaller groups in shallow water in areas of sand and rock. Locally the Pouting is known charmingly as the flobber!

Pollack *Pollachius pollachius*

Up to 1m (3.3ft). The Pollack is a slender, silver fish with a very distinct curved line along the side of its body. Young fish, which have a green-brown tinge, form shoals around areas of rock and hover above the kelp forest. Some individuals seem to prefer more sheltered areas as they get older and many of the Islands' wrecks have a few large, resident Pollack lurking in their shadows. Known locally as Whiting.

Greater Pipefish *Syngnathus acus*

Up to 47cm (18.5in). This fish is an olive-green to brown colour with darker bands and, like all other pipefish, it resembles an uncurled seahorse. It lives in areas of sand and weed down to about 20m (66ft) and can easily be approached, relying on its camouflage rather than its swimming abilities for protection. The male carries the eggs in his brood pouch and gives birth to about 400 fully-formed young which will return to his pouch in the first few days of life if danger threatens.

Short-Snouted Seahorse
Hippocampus hippocampus

Up to 12.5cm (5in). These enchanting fish appear in a wide variety of colours from brown and mauve to olive-green and yellow, and are able to 'flush' a paler colour in mating displays. They are thought to live mainly in eel grass beds but have been recorded in many different habitats and at all depths, including rock pools. Perhaps the most remarkable feature of the seahorse is the mating technique, in which the female passes the eggs to the male who fertilizes them in a special brood pouch. He provides them with nourishment as they grow and eventually gives birth to the fully-formed young.

Deep Snouted Pipefish
Syngnathus typhle

Up to 30cm (12in). As its name suggests, this pipefish has a long, deep snout which is flattened from side to side. Its light emerald-green colour helps it to blend perfectly with its preferred environment of the eel grass bed, a camouflage further aided by its habit of lying along the blades of the grass. Like all pipefish, and their relatives the seahorses, the males care for the eggs. In the summer they can be seen with their brood pouches bulging with growing young.

Snake Pipefish
Entelurus aequoreus

Females up to 60cm (24in), males up to 40cm (16in). The Snake Pipefish has a much smoother, more rounded body than the other pipefish and a tiny, almost non-existent tail. It is a beautiful golden brown colour with lighter silvery bands around its body and a red stripe through the eye. It lives amongst the weeds in rocky areas down to about 30m (100ft). The male carries the eggs attached to a hollow in his underside as he does not have a full brood pouch like many of the other pipefishes.

Sandsmelt *Atherina presbyter*

Up to 20cm (8in). The Sandsmelt is a slender fish with an iridescent silvery-green sheen. It is most often encountered at night when it is attracted by the lights of divers or fishermen. As it darts into the torch beam its body becomes almost completely transparent. It lives in fairly shallow water in sandy areas close to the shore and is known locally as 'grasdo'.

Fifteen-Spined Stickleback
Spinachia spinachia
Up to 20cm (8in). This stickleback is only found in the sea, unlike its three-spined relative which is equally at home in fresh water. It has a long, thin body and is a green-brown colour with stripes of cream and dark red on its face. As its name suggests, it has 15 spines along its back. This stickleback lives in rock pools and weedy areas down to about 10m (33ft).

Red Gurnard
Aspitrigla cuculus
Up to 40cm (16in). This fish is a brilliant pinky-red colour. It has a large head and a tapering body. The first few rays of its pectoral fins are modified to form a pair of finger-like feelers which it uses to walk around the sea bed and find its food. Gurnards often form small shoals and can be heard grunting to each other. All Gurnards have spectacular pectoral fins which they unfurl from their sides like fans. An individual with peacock blue markings on these fins is a Tub Gurnard, *Trigla lucerna*.

Long-Spined Sea Scorpion *Taurulus bubalis*
Up to 17.5cm (7in). The Sea Scorpion has a large head with spines on the cheek and a barbel at the corner of the mouth. Its colour varies to match its background making it very difficult to spot unless it moves. It lives in weedy and rocky areas down to 60m (200ft). Although the spines on the Sea Scorpion's back are sharp, they are not poisonous. The fish in the photograph has a parasitic crustacean on its head, often found on the Wrasse in Channel Island waters.

Bass

Dicentrachus labrax

Up to 1m (3.3ft). A large silver fish with very shiny, distinct scales, the Bass is found as deep as 100m (330ft), but in the summer it comes very close to the shore to spawn. Highly prized by fishermen and anglers, it is known as the 'salmon of the sea' and over-fishing has taken its toll on the local population in recent years. Bass seem to be attracted by anything that glints and the patient diver can be rewarded with very close encounters if he has something shiny with which to lure them.

Black Sea-Bream *Spondyliosoma cantharus*

Up to 50cm (20in). This oval-shaped silvery fish has an iridescent blue sheen to its scales. In the summer the males become very dark, hence their common name. The bream is a southern fish which migrates to the Channel Islands to breed in the summer, forming large shoals in rocky areas. It seems particularly fond of deep reefs, such as the Blanchard to the east of Sark. In the 1980s the numbers of these fishes dropped dramatically but now seem to be on the increase again.

Red Mullet *Mullus surmuletus*

Up to 40cm (16in). The colouring of the Red Mullet varies from yellow to red depending on the depth, the emotional state of the fish and the time of day. It has a pair of barbels under its chin which it flicks about in search of food in the sandy areas it prefers. When it senses something to eat the Red Mullet will dig frantically down into the sand, often almost completely disappearing. It is most often encountered by divers at night in the summer months.

Grey Mullet

Chelon labrosus

Up to 75cm (30in). The Grey Mullet is a blunt-nosed silver fish with faint horizontal stripes and very shiny, distinct scales. It is a bottom-feeder using its wide mouth to scoop up sand and mud from which it filters out any particles of food. It will also scrape green algae off rocks and pilings. Mullet live in shoals and are a common sight in shallow water all around the Channel Islands as well as in the harbours and marinas. In the winter, particularly large shoals gather close to the shores of Alderney.

Cuckoo Wrasse *Labrus bimaculatus*

Up to 35cm (14in). The Cuckoo Wrasse is certainly the most colourful fish in the waters around the Channel Islands. The female (see page 17) is a rose pink colour with a row of black and white bars on her back. The male is a striking mixture of turquoise blue and bright orange and can flash a white patch on his forehead to attract a mate. All Cuckoo Wrasse are born female, but between the ages of 7–13 some of them change into fully functional males. They are inquisitive, territorial fish that live around deep, rocky reefs.

Ballan Wrasse
Labrus bergylta

Up to 60cm (24in). The Ballan is the largest of the five species of wrasse found commonly in local waters. Its colours vary from orangey-browns to olive-greens with some of the young being bright green. The markings also vary, the younger fish having blotchy stripes and the older ones developing beautiful spots. They are shy fish and live in rocky areas with weed down to about 30m (100ft).

Corkwing Wrasse
Crenilabrus melops
Up to 20cm (8in). This wrasse is a bright olive-green colour with dark red 'marbling' and a characteristic dark spot in the centre of the tail stalk. It is common in shallow, weedy areas and sometimes gets stranded in rock pools. In the early summer the male builds an elaborate seaweed nest (see photograph) and lures the female in to lay her eggs which he then guards until they hatch. Like most of the wrasse, the Corkwing is known locally as rock fish.

Goldsinny Wrasse
Ctenolabrus rupestris
Up to 18cm (7in). The Goldsinny is a small, slim fish with a golden pink colour and a dark spot on the upper edge of the tail stalk. It lives in rocky areas at about 10–15m (33–50ft) and prefers to hide in crevices and small caves. The Goldsinny is a fairly inquisitive fish and the patient diver may be able to lure one out into the open by waving a shiny object.

Rock Cook
Centrolabrus exoletus

Up to 15cm (6in). This small, rounded fish is a red-brown colour with yellow sides and iridescent blue stripes on its face. It has an overall blue sheen which is even more pronounced in the male fish in the summer breeding season. There is also a dark stripe across the tail. The

Rock Cook is a shy fish and lives in small groups in the shelter of rocks and boulders down to about 25m (80ft). It is thought to clean parasites from other fishes.

Black-Face Blenny
Tripterygion delaisi

Up to 7cm (3in). As its name suggests, this fish has a very dark face and head. The female's body (below) is a mottled brown colour, making her difficult to spot in the

silty areas this fish prefers. The male (above) is much more conspicuous with an orangey-brown body and iridescent blue edges to his fins. In the spring he takes on his breeding colours and turns bright yellow. Black-face Blennies are very territorial and seem to prefer vertical rock faces below the low water line. This is another southerly species which is rarely seen north of the Channel Islands.

Tompot Blenny
Parablennius gattorugine
Up to 30cm (12in). Its large eyes, thick lips and the pair of tassels on its head give the Tompot Blenny an unmistakably comic appearance, an image strengthened by its habit of sitting propped up on its pelvic fins. It is a mottled orange-brown colour and lives in holes in rocky areas and on shipwrecks. This is an inquisitive, cheeky fish that will often rush out of its hole to nibble the fingers of a teasing diver.

Shanny
Lipophrys pholis
Up to 16cm (6in). The Shanny is a mottled green-brown colour and has a slimy skin with no scales. It lives in rocky areas down to 30m (100ft) and is often found in rock pools. It can even survive out of the water for several hours if stranded by the tide and can be seen wedged into shady cracks and crevices. Like all small, brown fish it is known locally as a 'cabot'.

Black Goby
Gobius niger
Up to 17cm (7in). Despite its name, the Black Goby is a sandy colour with darker blotchy spots. Its first dorsal fin is pointed, almost triangular, and has a dark spot, although this may be indistinct. This fish is common in eel grass, on sand and mud and in rock pools and is found at all depths. Like most gobies, the female lays her eggs in an empty shell or small crevice and the male guards them until they hatch.

Leopard Spotted Goby *Thorogobius ephippiatus*
Up to 13cm (7in). This fish has a pale, almost transparent body with dark brown blotchy spots. Its eyes are close-set on the top of the head and it has thick lips. It lives in rocky areas with plenty of cracks and crevices to hide in and seems happy to tolerate a certain amount of silt. This is a shy fish which sits on a ledge outside its hole into which it will disappear rapidly when approached.

Two Spot Goby
Gobiusculus flavescens

Up to 6cm (2.5in). This tiny fish is a reddish brown colour with a dark spot on the tail. The male has a second spot on the side, hence its name. In spring he also has beautiful iridescent blue markings on his fins to attract a mate, as shown in the photograph. Two Spot Gobies form small shoals in shallow water in rocky, kelpy areas and rock pools but their size makes them easy to overlook.

Dragonet *Callionymus lyra*

Males up to 30cm (12in), females up to 20cm (8in). The Dragonet is a bottom-living fish with a large head and a flattened, tapering body. Its light-brown mottled colouring makes it difficult to spot in the sandy areas it prefers, especially as it spends a great deal of time buried in the seabed with just its eyes uncovered. The male Dragonet is rarely seen but is much more colourful than the female with bright stripes of blue and yellow.

Shore Clingfish *Lepadogaster lepadogaster*

Up to 8cm (3in). The Clingfish is a red-brown colour with two blue spots on the back of its head and a fringed tentacle on the nose. It has a flattened head with a nose shaped like a duck's bill. On its underside a circle of fins forms the powerful sucker which it uses to stick to the underside of rocks. It lives in weedy areas but is more likely to be seen by lifting up rocks at low water than while diving.

Trigger Fish
Balistes carolinensis
Up to 50cm (20in). This grey-brown fish with bluish tints on its fins has a distinctive spiny dorsal fin which it uses to wedge itself into crevices when it feels threatened. The Trigger Fish feeds on crabs and other crustaceans and uses its very strong teeth and jaws to break them open. This is a warm water fish that comes into local waters during the summer but is not thought to breed here. It is most often seen by fishermen when it gets trapped in lobster pots trying to steal the contents.

Plaice
Pleuronectes platessa

Up to 90cm (35in). The Plaice is a light brown flat fish with characteristic bright orange spots. It lives in areas of sand and mud and spends much of the day buried in the seabed with just its eyes poking out. Like all flat fish, it spends the first few weeks of its life as a conventional 'round' fish. One eye then migrates around the top of the head next to the other one, the fish starts to swim on one side and then takes up its life on the sea bed.

Sole *Solea solea*

Up to 60cm (24in). The Sole is an oval-shaped fish with a mottled brown colour and darker blotches. It has a characteristic black spot on its pectoral fin which it leaves poking up when it buries itself in the sand. This is thought to resemble the poisonous fin of the Weever Fish and so wards off potential predators. The Sole lives in areas of sand and mud at all depths.

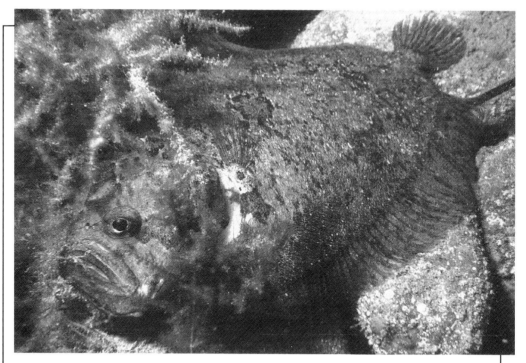

Topknot *Zeugopterus punctatus*

Up to 25cm (10in). The Topknot is the only flat fish to live in rocky areas where it clings to boulders and rocks. Its colouring can change to match its background but is basically brown with irregular dark blotches, a rough stripe running through the eye and a dark spot in the centre of the back. Its camouflage makes it difficult to spot but, once seen, it will stay completely still even if touched.

Useful addresses

Perhaps the best way to find out more about getting to the Channel Islands, the local dive centres, where to stay and where to visit, is to contact the relevant tourist information centre. The Islands' departments of agriculture and fisheries will be able to provide information about local fishing regulations.

Jersey Tourism Department
Liberation Square
St Helier
Jersey JE1 1BB
Tel 01534 500700

States of Guernsey Tourism Board
PO Box 23
St Peter Port
Guernsey GY1 3AN
Tel 01481 723552

Alderney Tourism Office
Victoria Street
St Anne
Alderney
Department
Tel 01481 823737

Sark Tourism
The Information Centre
Sark GY9 0SF
Tel 01481 832483

Jersey Department of Fisheries
PO Box 327
Howard Davis Farm
Trinity
Jersey JE4 8UF

States of Guernsey Seafisheries
Committee
Raymond Falla House
Longue Rue
St Martins
Guernsey
Tel 01481 35741

Marine Conservation Society
9 Gloucester Road
Ross-on-Wye
Herefordshire HR9 5BU

MCS Jersey Local Group
Charleston Cottage
Rue Rouge Cul
St Lawrence
Jersey JE3 1NP

Bibliography

The following books have been invaluable in the preparation of this book. I would recommend all of them to anyone wishing to further their knowledge of marine biology, particularly the books by Picton and Erwin, Dipper and Wood.

Ackers, R G, Moss, D, Picton, B E and Stone, S (1992) *Sponges of the British Isleas ('Sponge V)* Marine Conservation Society.

Cambell, A (1994) *Seashores and Shallow Seas of Britain and Europe,* Hamlyn.

Dipper, F A (1987) *British Sea Fishes,* Underwater World Publications Ltd.

Garrick-Maidment, N (1997) *Seahorses: Conservation and Care,* Kingdom Books.

Hayward, P J and Ryland, J S (1995) *Handbook of the Marine Fauna of Northwest Europe,* Oxford University Press.

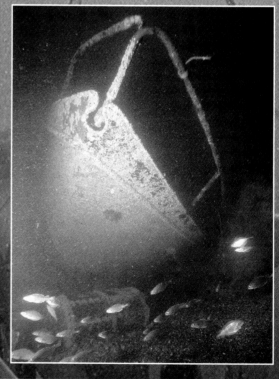

Chapter One

Howson, C M and Picton, B E (1997) *The Species Directory of the Marine Fauna and Flora of the British Isles.* Ulster Museum and Marine Conservation Society.

Kay, P and Young, A (1994) *Marine Wildlife of Atlantic Europe,* Immel Publishing.

Le Sueur, R F (1967) *The Marine Fishes of Jersey,* Société Jersiase.

Manuel, R L (1980) *The Anthozoa of the British Isles,* Marine Conservation Society.

Miller, P J and Loates, M J (1997) *Fish of Britain and Europe,* Harper Collins Publishers.

Naylor, P (1996) *Marine Animals of the South West,* Sound Diving Publications.

Picton, B E (1979) *Living Seashells: Molluscs of the English Channel and Atlantic Coasts,* Blandford Press.

Picton, B E (1985) *Ascidians of the British Isles,* Marine Conservation Society.

Picton, B E (1993) *A Field Guide to the Shallow Water Echinoderms of the British Isles,* Immel Publishing.

Picton, B E and Erwin, D (1987) *Guide to Inshore Marine Life,* Immel Publishing.

Picton, B E and Morrow, C C (1994) *A Field Guide to the Nudibranchs of the British Isles,* Immel Publishing.

Rowe, G (1995) *Common Life on the Seashore of the Channel Islands,* La Société Guernesiaise.

Sinel, J A (1905–1908) *A contribution to the knowledge of the Crustacea of the Channel Islands.* Société Guernesiase Transactions Vol. 5.

Sinel, J A (1906) *An Outline of the Natural History of Our Shores,* Swan Sonnenschein & Co.

Smaldon, G (1993) *Coastal Shrimps and Prawns,* Field Studies Council.

Wood, E (1988) *Sea Life of Britain & Ireland,* Immel Publishing.

Index

  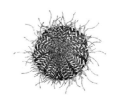